PINKFONG: BABY SHARK AND THE TOOTH FAIRY.
A CENTUM BOOK 978-1-912841-66-0
Published in Great Britain by Centum Books Ltd.
This edition published 2018.
1 3 5 7 9 10 8 6 4 2

Original Korean edition first published by Smart Study Co., Ltd.

This edition published by Centum Books Ltd in 2018 by arrangement with Smart Study Co., Ltd.

Centum Books Ltd, 20 Devon Square, Newton Abbot, Devon, TQ12 2HR, UK.

books@centumbooksltd.co.uk

CENTUM BOOKS Limited Reg. No. 07641486.

A CIP catalogue record for this book is available from the British Library.

Printed in Poland.

pinkfong

BABY SHARK
STORYBOOK SERIES

Baby Shark and the Tooth Fairy

centum

Baby Shark Family & Friends

Baby Shark

Baby Shark lives under the ocean and is curious about everything around him. He likes to sing. When he's scared, he sings to help him feel brave.

Mummy Shark

There are no limits to the things that Mummy Shark can do! She always listens to Baby Shark and they share a very special bond.

Daddy Shark

Daddy Shark is a strong and mighty hunter. He is much more than just Baby Shark's father though, the two of them play together like best friends!

The Tooth Fairy

The Tooth Fairy takes away weak, small teeth and leaves behind new, strong ones as a gift.

Grandma Shark

Grandma Shark likes to read. She is a kind and thoughtful grandma who always has time to spend with Baby Shark.

Grandpa Shark

Grandpa Shark is wise and smart. He is famous for his hot clam buns and he enjoys sharing his love of cooking with Baby Shark.

'Good morning!' says Baby Shark, beaming
with a smile as bright as the sun.
Wait a minute, is Baby Shark missing a tooth?

'Oh no! My tooth!'

Did Baby Shark put it somewhere to hide
it from tooth thieves?
Did Baby Shark put it somewhere safe until
he chomps down on his next hot clam bun?
'Oh no! I'm missing a tooth!' says Baby Shark.
Yes, Baby Shark, you are!

Is his missing tooth under this big rock?

Or is it hidden in this sandcastle?

Baby Shark looks here, there and everywhere!

'Where could it be?' wonders Baby Shark.

'Is it here?

At first, Baby Shark is mad that he's lost his tooth, and then he feels afraid.

'What am I going to tell Mummy Shark?
And what if I lose another?'

That night, Baby Shark had a dream that all his teeth ran away.

'Don't leave me toothless,' he cried.

But try as he might, Baby Shark could not catch his teeth.

Without any teeth, he looked just like his grandma!

The next morning when Baby Shark woke up, he still felt sad. He had no choice but to tell his mum the news.

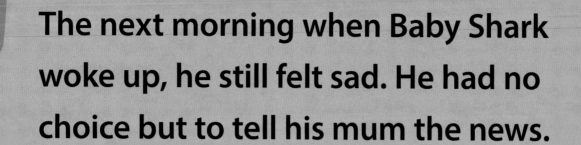

'Mum . . . Mum . . . I'm missing a tooth!'

'Oh, dear me! Don't worry, little one!' says Mummy Shark. 'The Tooth Fairy must have your missing tooth!'

'The Tooth Fairy?' asks Baby Shark.

'Yes, the Tooth Fairy takes the teeth you lose and brings you new ones,' says Mummy Shark.

Mummy Shark hugs Baby Shark tightly and starts to sing a song for him.

'Baby Shark, doo-doo-doo-doo-doo.

Sharp and bright
tooth-tooth-tooth-tooth- tooth.'

21

That night during his dreams, Baby Shark danced with the tooth fairy all night.

As Mummy Shark
had promised,
he got a new tooth,
so sharp and bright.

The next morning, Baby Shark saw his new tooth, and he couldn't stop smiling. 'It wasn't just a dream,' cries Baby Shark. 'The Tooth Fairy is real!'

Baby Shark swims straight to his mum.
'Mum, look at this! I've got a new tooth!'
says Baby Shark.

'What a wonderful tooth!'
says Mummy Shark.

'I won't worry so much the next time I lose a tooth!' says Baby Shark.

'See you then, Baby Shark!'
says the Tooth Fairy.